To Melissa—

May you have a year filled with peace, love, and happiness.

Love your forever friend,
Lisa 2020

**This book belongs to...**

*If you find this book taking time out to pause on its own,*
*I would be forever grateful if you could reunite us.*
*Good karma will come your way.*

This is an Axel & Ash book, part of the
'Insert Your Story' series. First Published in 2018.

We would love to see pictures of all the places that you take time out and *Press PAUSE* with your journal. Tag us on social media:

@axelandash #presspause #axelandash
www.axelandash.com | info@axelandash.com

**Publisher** Axel & Ash
**Creative Directors / Writers** Ashleigh Powell & Hanna Axelsson Sahlen
**Art Director & Designer** Jessica Wells
**Editor** Luanne Shneier
**Writer** Morgan Joanel
**Mandala Artist** Morgan Joanel
**Photography by** Alexandra Cohen, Arik Cardenas, Christian Schaffer, Daiton Vike, Daniel Smith, Elise Cook, Emma Carey, Elizabeth Rosa, Ellen Mary Taylor, Jacob Laub, Jemma Scott, Jillian Sun, Katie Purling, Lauren Williams, Marie-Hélène Vike, Matthew Morrissey, Melissa Gayle, Natalie Woods, Tracey Naughton, Thomas Davenport.

ISBN: 978-0-9874493-4-4

Printed in China.

# Pause.

**Pause / pɔ:z /**

*a short period in which something such as a sound or an activity is stopped before starting again.*

**Almost everything will work again if you unplug it for a**

few minutes, including you.

- Anne Lamott

Life is fast, wild, fun and exciting, but it's also often chaotic and stressful. We may be living great lives, but are we really there for them? Do we take the time to linger, enjoy, feel the real connections, listen to our bodies and notice the small moments that define our story? Many of us are seeking stillness in what has become a frantic world. Now, more than ever, we fail to live in the present.

*Press PAUSE* is a space for you to take time out each week and reflect on where you are. A place to stop, breathe, and celebrate your life as it is, but to also look back on what it was, who you are, who you want to be and where you want to go.

Journaling is one of the best tools to get in touch with yourself, and by putting pen to paper, we often realise things we didn't even know we thought and felt. Clearing your mind helps you dissolve stress, explore your creativity, make space for new ideas, and gives you the opportunity to plan out all those wild dreams and adventures to fulfil your life with.

This book is here for you to let go of the bullsh*t, celebrate the good sh*t and pay tribute to your unique strengths, quirks and general awesomeness. With space to jot down your soul goals and weekly thoughts, monthly check-in pages and prompts to dig deeper into your feelings, this is your time to slow down and be present with yourself.

So before you fast forward on life - pause, rewind and reflect on all the beautiful moments that can easily slip by. Once a week, curl up with your journal in your favourite spot to unplug, detach from the world and get lost in the most important journey of them all: your own.

It's time to Insert YOUR story! ♥

with love, Axel & Ash

# Current state *of mind...*

I got this book from

It made me think

My story right now

The time I currently take to pause and reflect

What I love most about my life

What I'd like to change

I'm excited to start to fill in this book because

# Currently...

I live

I work / study

I earn

My days are spent

My favourite people

A motto I live by

I spend too much time

I spend too little time

I keep putting off

I can't wait to

I want to learn

I want to experience

If I could live anywhere in the world

My dream job is

In one year, I see myself

In five years, my dream is to

In ten years, I think I

# soul goals

Mind & Spirit

Travel

Health

Career

Creativity & Passion

Finance

Organisation & Projects

Relationships

Life is a blank canvas and you're the artist. What will your masterpiece look like? This is your space to brainstorm all your dreams, ideas, plans and desires you want to colour your life with. Whether they're big or small, jotting down your goals will help you figure out exactly what lights your fire and what fulfils you in every sense = your soul goals.

Giving Back

Environment

# My game plan.

A goal without a plan is simply a wish. So, now that you've mapped out your soul goals, it's time to make your game plan to ensure these bad boys come alive. Looking at your mindmap, what are the six goals you would really like to focus on over the next 52 weeks? This is your space to jot them down and break each one down into small, realistic and manageable steps.

*PS - each month you'll be prompted with a little reminder to check in on how you're tracking with your plan.*

If you can't stop thinking about it - don't stop working for it!

-MICHAEL JORDAN

GOAL

*How I'll get it done*

GOAL

*How I'll get it done*

GOAL

*How I'll get it done*

GOAL

*How I'll get it done*

GOAL

*How I'll get it done*

GOAL

*How I'll get it done*

once she stopped rushing throu
she realised how much more life

IMAGE: @DAYONEFILMS

# week 01

*Date* ___ / ___ / ___

*Location* ___

I decided to start writing in my journal today because ___

Looking back on the week, I feel ___

Five moments I want to remember

1 ___

2 ___

3 ___

4 ___

5 ___

Something nice someone told me this week

Something pretty I saw

Exercise I did

An idea I thought of

Someone new I spoke to

I couldn't believe it when

A small moment that meant something big

*Let your mind run wild...*

When was the last time
you did something for the
first time? Flick to the back of
the book and start filling in
your bucket list. What do you
want to tick off first.?

# week
# 02

*Date* ___ / ___ / ___

*Location* ___

My week has been

Fun things that happened

Time spent in nature

Something weighing on my shoulders

# This week's...

Best morning

Favourite outfit

Most stressful moment

Funniest chat

Craziest day

Best dinner company

Most awkward moment

Sweetest compliment

Naughtiest treat

Biggest decision

If I could choose any superpower, it'd be

because

*slow.*

*Thoughts. Words. Scribbles. Pictures.*

# week 03

*Date* ____ / ____ / ____

*Location* ____

## This week I...

Loved ____

Helped ____

Had a great conversation with ____

Enjoyed ____

Got annoyed at ____ *Was it worth it?*

Joked with ____

Was attracted to ____

Had dinner with ____

Was inspired by ____

Was wrong about ____

Felt connected to ____

Thoughts that have been on my mind this week ____

A day at my job looks like

What I love about it

Things I would like to change

The step I want to take next in my career

Other dream jobs

If I could change jobs for one week, I would

## relationship goals

*Life moves by quickly and it's so easy to get lost in our own lives. Hours become days, weeks become years and after a while, our connections can weaken. We waste so much time scrolling our feeds and getting entertained by things that don't matter and people we don't really know. But what about the real relationships in our world? The ones that really matter? Are we dedicating enough time to nourishing our connections with the people we actually care about?*

My relationship with my family is

What I value most in my family

My relationships with my friends are

What I value most in my friends

My relationship with my partner is

What I value most in my partner

A relationship that I miss

Things I'd like to improve in my relationships

Thoughtful or fun things I want to do for (or with) my family and friends

Date / /

Location

# week 04

Monday was

Tuesday I

Wednesday felt

Thursday I went

Friday I saw

Saturday I rocked

Sunday was spent

This week, I'm grateful for

Moments that I want to remember

Something I've thought a lot about lately

It made me realise

What lights my fire

stop, rewind & record

# Monthly Reflection

Something, someone or somewhere new

Moments that meant that little something extra

Am I kicking my soul goals? This month I've worked on

Someone I can reach out to for guidance to achieve my goals

Something I've learned

Advice to myself for the next month

X X X

# week
# 05

*Date* / /

*Location*

Magical moments of the week

Emotion of the week

Song of the week

Challenge of the week

Hero of the week

Restaurants I've visited lately

Restaurants I want to try

My favourite band or artist at the moment

Lyrics I love

Last good deed I did

Last time I laughed 'til I cried

I believe everyday should have at least one exquisite moment.

Audrey Hepburn

# week
# 06

*Date* ____ / ____ / ____

*Location* ________

My week in words

I spent too much time on

I didn't spend enough time on

I felt amazing when

I felt challenged by

I daydreamed about

I learned that

I really wonder if

The World is Our

IMAGE: @ELLENMARYTAYLOR

week

# 07

*Date* ___/___/___

*Location* ___

## This week I...

Hit snooze

Hugged

Kissed

Watched

Unplugged

Practiced

Was late to

Cooked

Read

Planned

Missed

Failed to

Lied about

Regretted

Smiled

Dreamed

Cleaned

Helped

Recent news that made me happy

Recent news that made me sad

People who support or believe in me

Skills or talents I'm not using

If I had a magic wand right now, my top three wishes would be

1.

2.

3.

I want to be remembered for

Unplug. Challenge yourself to a tech-free day. No phone, no computer, no internet, no TV for a whole 24 hours. Let's see what mischief you can get up too when nobody can connect to you.

# week 08

*Date* / /

*Location*

Things that excited me this week

A situation that made me feel uncomfortable

I dealt with it by

If I could do something differently, I would

My favourite person this week

because

The best dining experience

because

The funniest moment

because

Something that made me feel warm inside

If I could give myself a piece of advice at the start of this week, it would be

stop, rewind & record

# Monthly Reflection

Something, someone or somewhere new

Moments that meant that little something extra

Am I kicking my soul goals? This month I've worked on

Something I regret

Something I've learned

Advice to myself for the next month

X X X

*Date* / /

*Location*

# week 09

The week summed up in three words

My work/life balance this week was

Something out of the ordinary I did

I spent a lot of time thinking about

I was feeling at total bliss when

I keep putting off

# The person in my life who's the most...

Inspiring

Adventurous

Witty

Loud

Hangry

Negative

Chilled

Thoughtful

Intelligent

Quirky

Ambitious

Weird

Something sweet I did for someone lately

Something sweet someone did for me

Lessons I'm learning right now

## body & soul

*Isn't it amazing how we are creatures of atoms and molecules, given this one magical life? Connecting with our body and taking care of our health is the best investment we can make in affecting how long we get to stay and play. Stress, sleep, exercise and diet all play a huge role in how you feel and the quality of life you have. So make sure that you listen to, love and respect this one beautiful body you've been given in every way possible.*

How healthy do I feel right now? ____________________

____________________

____________________

### To take care of my body and soul, I...

Exercise ____________________

____________________

Eat ____________________

____________________

Practice mindfulness ____________________

____________________

On average, I get ______ hours of sleep, per night.

My stress levels are ____________________

____________________

I feel the healthiest when ____________________

____________________

Things I'd like to improve on to make me feel, look and function better ____________________

____________________

____________________

To reach them I need to ____________________

____________________

____________________

Take some time to really stop and listen to your body - what is it telling you? Do you constantly have a sore back? Stomach pains? Is your skin breaking out? A lot of this comes from the inside and how we treat our bodies. Don't ignore the signs!

# The girl who fell from the sky.

What would you do differently if you knew that your life would change forever in a single moment? That everything you had planned and dreamed of was taken away?

This was a reality for Em Carey, one of the most inspiring, optimistic and bubbly girls out there. This is her story...

*Isn't it crazy how life is one thing and then in a single moment it becomes something entirely different? That's how it happened for me anyway. Here I was, Emma, the girl who loves to run and travel the world and whose biggest worry is what I was having for dinner that night. And then in an instant, everything changed. A freak skydiving accident is what did it for me. I was falling to what I presumed would be my death, but instead I landed to the realisation that I was completely paralysed from the waist down.*

*From that moment, I wasn't the same girl anymore. Not only did my physical body change, but so did my mind and the essence of who I am. When something like this happens, I believe we have two choices. We can let it ruin us, or we can use the pain as fuel to create the greatest life we have ever known. Me being a hopeless optimistic, I chose the second option and to this day it's the greatest thing I've ever done. My only regret is that it took me nearly dying to open my eyes and change my life.*

*I don't think we should have to go through something so traumatic just to realise the beauty around us. Don't wait for something dramatic to change your life. There is so much happiness waiting for you, there is so much more good in the world than bad, and there is so much light after darkness if you are willing to create it.*

**Em, can you tell us a bit about your life before the accident?** I was just an ordinary twenty year old girl saving to travel. I didn't know what I wanted to do. I just had an idea I wanted to travel.

**Where were you planning to go?** I was going with my best friend Jemma and we didn't even have a return ticket. It was our first big trip together and we were just backpacking around Europe with no set plans.

**Young, wild and free, you decided to go skydiving. What happened that day?** I was such an adrenaline junkie and I always wanted to go skydiving in this one spot in Switzerland. I wasn't scared or nervous - just so excited. When we jumped out of the helicopter, I remember the free fall being the most amazing feeling in the whole world. And then it all started to go wrong. The chords came out and wrapped around the instructor's neck and strangled him unconscious. The parachute was tangled and we just fell really fast - I was 100% certain we were going to die. I landed on my belly and he landed on my back. He was unconscious and not responding, so I tried to get up to get help but I couldn't move and that's when I realised that everything from the waist down was paralysed. I had broken my back, pelvis, sternum, my jaw and all my teeth were shattered. It was the scariest thing I've ever felt–just a moment earlier I was a twenty year-old girl without a worry in the world, living life backpacking around Europe. And literally a minute later, I saw my future in a wheelchair and life would be completely different from there on.

**You were told you would never be able to walk again, but you can walk now and just completed the 'Wings for Life' 5km run. How did this happen?** Yes, I am very lucky. After a lot of rehab I can walk now, but it's still not easy. People often tell me it's because I stay positive all the time, but I don't think it's fair to say that was the reason. I think I just got really lucky on how my spinal cord was injured. It was a big dream to complete a marathon, because after being told 'you're never going to be able to walk again', it's kind of the ultimate. I can't run well because my calves don't work and they're what you use to get a spring in your step, so it's very flat footed. So I started with a 5km and trained really hard, but it was the hardest thing ever and I realised that it will take a lot of time to build my leg strength - but one day I'd definitely love to do a full marathon.

**What are some of the struggles you deal with daily?** Many things I go through seem really hard, but have become part of my everyday life. Like, I can't feel my legs or if I am hurting them, which means I get a lot of scrapes, cuts and burns. I can't feel the pain and they take a really long time to heal. But the main thing is that my bladder and bowels don't work at all, so I need to use catheters and enemas, as I have no idea when I need to go to the bathroom - which means I pee myself all the time.

**You're incredibly honest, raw and real about the challenges you face. What advice would you give to others who struggle to open up?** Everyone has something they get embarrassed about. I remember>

thinking, "if I'm going to get upset or embarrassed every time I pee myself, it would mean I'll be upset 20 times a day, every day for the rest of my life. Do I want to spend the rest of my life embarrassed? No." I realised pretty early on that I would have to change my reactions, otherwise I wouldn't have a very good life. My advice would be to tell the people around you whatever problems you face so you can talk about it, deal with it together and have a laugh about it. Honesty is definitely the most important thing.

**Your mantra is 'if you can, you must.' What does this mean?** A few days after the accident, I was lying in bed and I wrote a note saying 'if you can, you must'. I was thinking about running and how I took it for granted. The morning of the skydive, my friend and I were meant to go for a run around the Swiss Alps, but I was being lazy and thinking, "I can't be bothered, I'll do it tomorrow". I just felt so much regret that I could have gone for a run that morning, but chose not to and then later that day I was told I will never walk, let alone ever run again. I said to myself 'if you can ever run again, you must'. It applies to so many other things in life and is a reminder to do things while you can because you never know when it's your last chance to do it.

**What has been the biggest change in your life since you got a second chance?** Before it, I lacked appreciation and gratitude, and it just never occurred to me that I should be grateful for simple things like my body, my health and my legs. It just seemed like my body was always going to work. When I was falling, I genuinely thought I was going to die and only having seconds to live before I hit the ground really made me realise just how much I loved my life and how precious it is. While it sucked at the time, if I hadn't had the accident I don't think I would have stopped to think about what's truly important in life. I now have an appreciation and gratitude for everything: life itself, my mind, my body. Before my accident, I would just look at a sunset and be like, 'ok that's cool' but now I can really feel how special it is and how lucky I am to get to experience it.

**You really found a way to see beauty in everything. How important is it to take time to pause to find your true self?** It's very important because people just go through the motions of everyday - getting up, going to work, coming home - without stopping to think. You can go through years without ever questioning or thinking "is there something I would enjoy more, is this the best way to spend my time, are my friends good to me?" Unless you stop and have an outside perspective on your life, you could go decades living a life that isn't necessarily the best one for you.

**We discovered you through your amazing art. Can you tell us a bit more about it?** It only started after my accident when I was in hospital. Being stuck in bed, I didn't have much else to do so I started doodling and drawing 'thank you' cards for my nurses. Over time I began to post pictures online and people started asking me where they could buy them. It kind of happened naturally from the accident which is nice.

**How do you spend your days now?** My art is now my main job. I also do bit of writing and started doing speaking gigs which I really love. Day-to-day, I always do some form of rehab, exercise, play with my niece (she's the cutest) and just try to make the most out of everyday doing things I really enjoy doing.

**You've said that instagram is like a journal for you. How so?** Writing kind of makes me realise my thoughts before I even really understand them myself. It's really therapeutic and helps things make more sense in my head. I used Instagram a bit like a diary and wrote what I was feeling through my recovery and the lessons I'd learned. People started to resonate with the honesty and even if they couldn't necessary relate to my exact struggles, they could resonate with the feelings associated.

**We heard that you love the mind of a child?** Yeah, when I look at my niece, she is always so happy, laughing and doesn't have worries of what people think of her or what will happen in the future. Kids are just so present. Adults are accustomed to thinking and worrying a bit more. Being present like a child is a really nice way to look at the world - see things for exactly what they are, without pain or worry.

**Three people you would like to invite to a dinner party?** Ellen DeGeneres, Taylor Swift and Turia Pitt. Turia was badly burnt in a bushfire - I read her book and listened to a lot of her talks and she's just like the most inspiring person ever!

**Tell us a quirky thing about you.** I hate weirdly sized fruits and vegetables. If they're super small or big for their own normal size, like massive capsicums or tiny grapes - disgusting.

**What are some of your dreams for the next five to ten years?** I really want to finish writing a book I'm working on in the next year. I feel very compelled to share my story and to pass on things I've learned from my near-death experience. I'd also love to do more talks, travel and hopefully meet my husband.

**What's the best advice you've ever received?** My skydive instructor said to me after the accident, "your body won't heal unless your mind does." I never thought about it at the time, but now I see that it's so important to have a good mindset so everything else in your life flows. ♥

*Em's bucket list*

- x LEARN TO SKATEBOARD
- x GO TRAVELLING ON MY OWN
- x RUN THE NYC MARATHON
- x LEARN SPANISH
- x GO TO AN ELLEN SHOW

Check out Em's art, jewellery and miraculous journey @em_carey

Date / /

Location

# week 10

This week I

The biggest challenge

The grumpy moments

Things that made me laugh

Small wins I had this week

*Lots of small wins = a big win!*

Personal projects I worked on

Skills I want to learn

If I could make a living doing anything, I would

How can I make it happen?

The last time I did something for the first time

Something new I want to try next week

# week 11

*Date* / /

*Location*

The start of the week

The end of the week

Highlight of the week

Overheard this week

Lunch of the week

Things I said yes to this week

Things I said no to this week

# My mind dump...

*What's cluttering your mind? A mental to-do list? Thoughts? Feelings? Ideas you've never put into action? Whether they've been at the back of your mind for months (like putting up that frame) or a brilliant idea you thought of this week, this is your space to write them all down. Getting it all out on paper will make you feel clearer, calmer and more focused so you can concentrate on new things.*

IMAGE: @LETMESEA

it's full of answers

# week 12

*Date* ___ / ___ / ___

*Location* ___

This week's highs

This week's lows

I indulged in

I was tempted to

My biggest priorities in life right now

An ambitious goal I want to achieve

Three places I went this week

1

2

3

Five things I want to do and explore in my own city

1

2

3

4

5

Last time I got lost

Last time I spoke to a stranger

stop, rewind & record

# Monthly Reflection

Something, someone or somewhere new

Moments that meant that little something extra

Am I kicking my soul goals? This month I've worked on

I was inspired by

Something I've learned

Advice to myself for the next month

X X X

*Date* ____ / ____ / ____

*Location* ____

# week 13

## This week I...

Felt

Loved

Achieved

Tried

Watched

Disliked

Admired

Decided to

Worked on

Couldn't stop

Ate too much

Was embarrassed by

Watched the sunrise / sunset

Cuddled with

Was surprised by

## Three people I adore...

Name

Because

Name

Because

Name

Because

*Have you told them? If not, make sure they know.*

exhale.

*Thoughts. Words. Scribbles. Pictures.*

# week 14

*Date* / /

*Location*

This week's encounters

A story I heard

A heated moment

A compliment I gave

A secret

Three things on my bucket list I want to tick off next...

1.

I want to do this because

2.

This idea came from

3.

Ticking this off will feel

## What's stopping you? Let's start planning!

How I'm going to make each one happen

1.

2.

3.

Five things I can do next week to get the ball rolling...

1.
2.
3.
4.
5.

## counting my pennies

*It's so easy to lose sight of where our money goes. But, if we take a moment to pause and reflect on our finances, it can make a big difference. A little bit of planning can go a long way in helping us reach some of our dreams. So, if you don't have a budget or game plan, now's the perfect time to start.*

My current financial situation is

How conscious am I of where my money goes?

Things I would like to save my pennies for

How much I need

Expenses I could avoid

How much I could save in a year

Luxuries I don't mind spending on

Am I willing to pull back on my luxuries to reach my savings goals?

My financial goals for the next 52 weeks are

**At 23, JK Rowling was broke. Tina Fey was working at the Y.M.C.A. Oprah had just gotten fired from her first job as a TV reporter and Walt Disney had declared bankruptcy. Everything will be ok!**

IMAGE: @ALEXCOHEN

# week 15

*Date* / /

*Location*

This week I'm proud of

I felt appreciated by

I ventured outside to

My stress levels were

My last holiday was

*is it time for another one?*

# The last...

Shoes I wore

Restaurant meal

Person I spoke to

Exercise I did

Toilet I visited

Time I travelled

Item I purchased

Book I read

Machine I used

Live show I saw

Time I cried

Song I heard

Hug

Kiss

Face I admired

Time I slept in

Lie I told

Film I saw

Wild experience

Message I sent

*Work like a captain.*
*Play like a pirate.*

IMAGE: @LOZYJANE

# week 16

*Date* ____/____/____

*Location* ____________

The best morning this week ____________

The most awkward moment ____________

My concentration levels have been ____________

I was proud as punch when ____________

I laughed with ____________

I am feeling lots of love for ____________

I couldn't help thinking ____________

Favourite outfit I wore ____________

Someone close to me that I want to surprise

Nothing makes me happier than

The last person I hugged

## Best advice I've ever gotten from...

My grandparents

My dad

My sibling(s)

My mum

My best friend

# Monthly Reflection

Something, someone or somewhere new

Moments that meant that little something extra

Am I kicking my soul goals? This month I've worked on

Someone I can reach out to for guidance to achieve my goals?

Something I've learned

Advice to myself for the next month

X X X

# week 17

*Date* / /

*Location*

This week I

The most beautiful morning was

The best afternoon

The cosiest night

Something I did, but wish I didn't

People who've made a huge difference in my life, and why

How can I pay it forward

My 'happy place' is

My perfect day looks like

I can't wait until

*Date* / /

*Location*

# week 18

## This week I...

Saw

Heard

Smelled

Felt

Tasted

Sensed

# Currently...

Sitting

Wearing

Missing

Hoping

Amazed by

Addicted to

Intimidated by

Craving

Wondering if

In love with

Worried about

Excited to

Pick a cookbook and try a new recipe every week for the next month. Invite someone over to share it with.

Date / /

Location

# week 19

This week's vibe

Snapshots of the week

Fun times I had

Interesting discussions

My favourite weekly rituals

Some of the things I've complained about lately

Were they really worth complaining about?

Why?

A project I really want to do, but keep pushing back

What's stopping me?

*Make an action plan to make it happen!*

Next week I want to

Next week, be a tourist in your own city. Head to a spot you've always wanted to explore.

# find your true north

When you hear the word 'wanderlust', what images are conjured up in your mind? Ideas of travelling the world? Beautiful bohemian visuals of the wild and free? Or maybe even yoga set amongst a backdrop of the mountains with a music festival vibe? That last one is thanks to Schuyler Grant, co-founder of the Wanderlust Festivals - a celebration of mindful living that merges yoga, music, the arts, food and meditation into a four day immersive experience.

It's obvious when talking with Schuyler that her rebellious nature and drive to serve others was always going to be the perfect mix to create a global event like *Wanderlust*. Stretching from incredible places like Lake Tahoe in North America to Nagoya in Japan, she's helped shape a global health and wellness event that truly embraces the power of pausing and being present in the moment.

If you had told 14-year-old Schuyler what she would be doing today, she would've thought that you were absolutely crazy. The Californian mother of three beautiful girls grew up in a hippie community in the 1970's, with parents who lived off the land and practiced yoga daily. Raised in this environment, Schuyler did a 180 and moved east to *Columbia University*. She saw yoga as a strange thing her parents did and never would have imagined that it would be a pivotal part of her future.

It wasn't until her mid-twenties that Schuyler began practicing Ashtanga yoga, purely as a physical attempt to heal chronic pain. She wasn't seeking anything spiritual or profound when she first started, but her back did begin to heal and - as with most things needing to be called into consciousness - it was through stillness that everything began to shift quietly into place.

**Schuyler, you're the founder of a legendary festival celebrated worldwide - can you tell us a bit about your childhood?** I grew up in Northern California in a pretty deep hippie environment in a semi-communal situation. But my dad's family is from the East Coast, from a traditional 'WASPy' family and we all spent our summers there. I had a pretty schizophrenic upbringing between 'barefoot and dirty' for nine months of the year and then in little pinafore dresses and white patent leather shoes for three months over summer. That turned me into the totally confused adult I am!

**So, your parents introduced you to yoga?**
My parents were part of that whole movement of the classic 60's generation. They lived super sustainably and close to the land, built their own house, bought second-hand and had almost zero waste. My parents would get up in the morning to meditate, stretch and do simple yoga poses, but there was a lot of burping and flatulence involved so I just thought yoga was the grossest thing. If you asked me when I was 14 if I would be a yoga teacher or open a yoga studio, I would have thought you were out of your mind.

**How did you end up getting into yoga then?**
I was in a car accident as a kid, and in my teens I had chronic back pain. So after I left home, I started doing Ashtanga style yoga which is a really straightforward series of postures with no overt spirituality attached. Then I was like, "Wow, what is this I am feeling?" I felt shifted. I felt openness, intention, achievement and connection to... something... some might call it God or just meta consciousness.

**Since then, you've opened four yoga studios, your first being *Kula Yoga* in NYC. What made you open your own?** After September 11, everyone in the city was doing something to help and serve. I thought, "Well, yoga has helped me so much, we should open a yoga studio in Tribeca - it will be a little side project, just a great offering". It was so much more work than I ever envisioned!

**How powerful is the connection between the body and the mind?** In my experience, the body is the most effective way to change the mind- rather than the mind changing the body. Some people use the mind - through meditation - to effect states of higher consciousness, in yoga the body and the breath are the tools. And then there is a feedback loop, the brain informs the breath, which moves the body, which talks back to the mind, and round and round. >

**You went from thinking yoga was weird, to starting the world's largest yoga festival with your husband and friend. How did you all meet?** We were three best friends from college. My husband Jeff and Sean started a music/jazz/hip-hop music label in Tribeca, and then I ended up opening my yoga studio in the same building as them right after 9/11. I was a film editor at that time and was practicing Yoga, but had no intentions of being a full-time yoga teacher.

**How did the idea for *Wanderlust* first come about?** The music industry started crumbling when digitalization came along, at the exact moment that wellness was starting to become a legitimate industry. Jeff and Sean saw how people were hiking up to my funky little 4th floor yoga studio as they were struggling to find money to produce the next record. I often led yoga retreats in Costa Rica and they would come and be like, "this is so fun, and these people are *so normal*". At one point, Jeff was like "You could totally make a music festival for this crowd".

**What did you envision *Wanderlust* to be?** Our vision was to take a large-scale music festival and mix it with the wellness world to create a transformative experience. We wanted to make something that had the depth and integrity from a yoga, meditation and holistic health standpoint, and put it in nature, which is such a key component to actually shifting peoples' perspective. To put yourself somewhere else - somewhere extraordinary and beautiful - it makes you realize how much larger nature and the cosmos is than you. It was a totally new concept back then. The term 'yoga festival' had not yet been coined.

**What actually happens at a *Wanderlust* festival?** Going to *Wanderlust* is a pause in its own expansive way. It's celebration of mindful living in the midst of some of the most breathtaking natural settings imaginable. The focus is on yoga, meditation, outdoor adventuring, clean foods, local wine and beer, and of course music. You program your days with yoga classes from pretty much every tradition, more subtle practices like meditation breathwork and sound healing, guided hikes, runs and stand up paddleboarding, and lectures. Evenings are looser and you can choose from farm to table dinners, picnics, wine tastings, avant-garde performances under the stars and a whole slew of DJs and live music. It's a pretty magical bubble - a four day pause from the world - where you come with your past but leave with your future.

**You have festivals all over the globe now. What role do you play these days?** I live in LA and I'm the National Director of Yoga for *Wanderlust*. I help run the big flagship center in Hollywood, heading up the yoga program. I have a small part in helping run and program the festivals - more of an advisory role to help curate the yoga experience. I also co-direct *Kula's* 3 studios in NYC, teach public classes and workshops, and lead advanced teacher trainings, which is my biggest passion.

**The *Wanderlust* tagline is 'Find Your True North'. What does this mean?** Every life needs a compass. No matter where you take a compass, it's going to show true north. All of us need tools to help us figure out what an authentically meaningful life looks like. *Wanderlust* hopes to expose people to the practices that help them lead purpose filled lives.

**To pause - what does it mean to you?** Pausing is anything you do, where there is no past or future, where you are truly present. That experience can happen in so many different ways - but one of the most reliable conduits to experiencing the moment is the mind-body arts.

**How important do you think it is to pause in order to find your true north?** It is imperative. We never get anywhere if we just spin our wheels. That's really what it is - kids are often on pause, that's why adults spend so much of their life trying to find their 'child mind'. Trying to recreate the place where we are not in the past or the future. I would say in a multitude of ways, *Wanderlust* is trying to be that place.

**How does it feel to know you're impacting people's lives so positively?** Since the beginning the experience has been super fun, but also genuinely transformational. People go home saying, "I am going to marry that guy - or leave that guy - or quit that job - or start that business." There are so many *Wanderlust* babies out there - you wouldn't believe it! People who met at *Wanderlust* have come back and gotten married at the festival years later. We're constantly amazed. It's a privilege to provide the container for that shift in someone's life.

**What advice can you share to someone looking to find the best version of themself?** More nature - and I don't mean half-baked nature, I mean get out of the city and get deep into nature. It's difficult to not get the bigger picture when you're in the bigger picture!

**If you could make one change in the world, what would it be?** That is so easy. I would remove any repercussions of carbon on the atmosphere and any destruction on the environment. I'd change the human destructive relationship to nature. We are polluting our own backyard and we are killing ourselves - it breaks my heart everyday. ♥

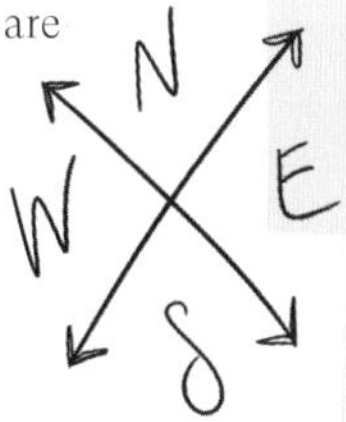

Check out @wanderlustfest to attend one of these rad festivals.

## Short & sweet

**Wanderlust. What does the word mean to you?** A quest for spiritual travel and search to know one's self.

**Do you think change from within is possible?** Absolutely, otherwise I'd be a corporate lawyer.

**What is your mantra?** My mantra is 'everything in moderation, including moderation'.

**Favourite things about your husband?** He's so funny and he smells like baked bread.

**The cafes or restaurants we'll find you at?** Marlow and Sons in NYC or Pace in L.A

**Any must reads?** The Absolutely True Diary of a Part-time Indian

**Three pieces of advice you'd give your daughters?**

- Make sure you work at something you love
- Make sure any partner you have, male or female, changes as many diapers as you do
- Live more lightly on the planet than your parents do

# week
# 20

*Date* / /

*Location*

This week's experiences

Small, everyday things that made me smile

Recent successes I've had

The last setback I had to deal with

People who've helped me lately

People I've helped

Quote of the week

Three small acts of kindness I'm going to do next week

1.

2.

3.

**stop, rewind & record**

# Monthly Reflection

Something, someone or somewhere new

Moments that meant that little something extra

Am I kicking my soul goals? This month I've worked on

Something I regret

Something I've learned

Advice to myself for the next month

X X X

Date / /

Location

# week 21

Seven memories from this week

Moments spent in nature

Something new I learned

Three things I'm grateful for

1

2

3

Five people I'd really like to meet and why

## fearlessly me

*One of the most attractive qualities in a person is confidence. When you're genuinely content and at peace with who you are, you make no excuses for simply being you. Whether you're loud, shy, bubbly, awkward, or just have a different take on the world to the people around you, owning who you are radiates charisma, confidence and an authenticity that inspires the people around you. Remember there is only one you - so fearlessly be yourself.*

How confident do I feel within myself?

Do I worry about how others see me?

Situations that make me feel uncomfortable

Do I compare myself to others? If so, how?

Am I confident to stand up for my own thoughts, opinions and feelings

Things I don't feel confident about and want to change

Now, give your soul a cuddle and jot down a few things you love about yourself

**A flower does not think of competing with the flower next to it. It just blooms.** - *Zen Shin*

Follow your soul...
it knows the way.
- Ritu Rai

IMAGE: @ELLENMARYTAYLOR

# week 22

*Date* ___ / ___ / ___

*Location* ___

Best parts of this week

Best breakfast

Best lunch

Best dinner

Goals I've kicked

I felt a little overwhelmed by

To get more organised, I need to

# The last time I...

Went to the dentist

Laid in the sunshine

Went for a long run

Meditated / Practised yoga

Swam in the ocean

Donated blood

Disagreed with someone

Went for a skin check

Finished reading a book

Got up for a sunrise

## Next week, I'm really looking forward to...

Seeing/meeting

Going

Surprising

Playing

*reflect.*

*Thoughts. Words. Scribbles. Pictures.*

Date ____ / ____ / ____

Location ____

# week 23

The first five moments that pop into my head when I look back on the week

1

2

3

4

5

The last time I was really hurt

It hurt me because

How am I contributing to this situation?

*Is it due to my insecurities? Different values? Misunderstandings?*

Have I done something to try change the situation?

Someone who made me smile this week

Where, When, Why?

An old friend I want to reconnect with

It's time to learn
something new! Sign
up for that course or
class that you've been
intrigued to try.

# week
# 24

*Date* / /

*Location*

A moment I loved this week

A moment I didn't give a damn

An event I attended recently

A book/film/podcast I enjoyed

A disappointing moment

A problem I have

A good deed

A person I met

A person I want to meet

A person I want to get to know better

*Why not invite them over for dinner?*

A recipe I want to try

A home project I want to start / complete

A friend I miss

*Is it time for you to call them?*

A personal trait I want to adopt

A change I've made within myself

stop, rewind & record

# Monthly Reflection

Something, someone or somewhere new

Moments that meant that little something extra

Am I kicking my soul goals? This month I've worked on

I was inspired by

Something I've learned

Advice to myself for the next month

X X X

Date / /

Location

# week 25

What's my routine been like this week?

Things I've done outside of my normal routine

An interesting conversation I had

Someone that made me smile, and why

A loving gesture, I received

What have I been avoiding due to fear of failure?

Do I worry about what others think?

What signs have I been misinterpreting or ignoring?

What am I curious about?

What brings me joy?

I'd like to attract

One is never alone with a book nearby. Ask a friend for their best recommendation- whether an old classic or something new - and make a commitment to read it.

# week 26

*Date* ___ / ___ / ___

*Location* ___

Six months have passed since I started taking time to pause weekly. I've...

Noticed

Learned

Felt

Changed

The best things that have happened to me in the last six months are

Reflecting on my life, thoughts and dreams make me

In the next six months, I want to make sure I...

__________ more, and __________ less

Visit __________

__________

Enjoy __________

__________

Cook __________

__________

See more __________

__________

Spend time __________

__________

Take __________

__________

Stop __________

__________

Start __________

__________

My goals to make sure the next six months are amazing __________

__________

__________

__________

__________

__________

## stress less

*Stress. We all experience it, but it manifests in different ways for everyone. Muscle tension, insomnia, headaches, or that tight, anxious feeling in your gut - all of which can affect our relationships, health and wellbeing in harmful ways. Our brains often don't know the difference between a real threat and our imagination, leading it to send out signals that we feel as stress, anxiety and worry even when we're not in danger. It's sometimes hard to identify and understand what causes these symptoms, but once we understand where our stress stems from, we can learn to cope better and take control.*

How organised and in control of my life am I right now?

On a scale of 1 to 10 (with 1 being not at all and 10 being extremely), how stressed am I?

1 2 3 4 5 6 7 8 9 10

Things that constantly stress me out or make me feel anxious

Why? What are the reasons behind me being stressed and anxious in these situations?

A few things I worry about, that I probably shouldn't

To relax and alleviate my stress and worries, I

The next time you are feeling stressed, anxious or worried, take four long, deep breaths and ask yourself these questions.

*1. What am I actually afraid of?*

*2. What is the worst that can happen?*

*3. What can I do about it right now that will help alleviate the feeling?*

# week 27

*Date* / /

*Location*

Seven moments from the past seven days

1

2

3

4

5

6

7

Something I did for myself this week

Something I wish I'd done differently

This week I was proud of

A bad habit I want to get rid of

My body is telling me

A nice thing I did for someone else

Something I want to do more of

# week 28

*Date* ___/___/___

*Location* ___

The most amazing moments this week

The most random moment

The tastiest thing I ate

The biggest fear that crossed my mind

The funniest thing that happened

Criticism I received

An interesting conversation I had this week

Talking about it made me think and feel

Next week, I want to prioritise

I'm super excited about

**stop, rewind & record**

# Monthly Reflection

Something, someone or somewhere new

Moments that meant that little something extra

Am I kicking my soul goals? This month I've worked on

Someone I can reach out to for guidance to achieve my goals?

Something I've learned

Advice to myself for the next month

X X X

We live on a blue planet that
circles around a ball of fire
next to a moon that moves the sea,
and you don't believe in miracles?

IMAGE: @ATLASDARLINGS

Date ____ / ____ / ____

Location ____

# week 29

My three favourite moments this week

1

2

3

## The last time I felt...

Sad

Proud

Overwhelmed

Curious

Spontaneous

Bossy

Confident

Jealous

Wild

If I could find out one thing about my future, I'd love to know

If I could turn back time

If I could change something about last week

There's nothing like hearing a familiar voice. Call up an old friend or relative that you've lost touch with and reconnect.

# sunday escapes

## *a promise to adventure*

**Have you ever dreamed of packing it all up to taste the freedom of hitting the road, sleeping under the stars and living life in the slow lane? That's exactly what Dom and Elise Cook did, a lovestruck, free-spirited couple who made this bohemian fairytale their reality. With their wild curls and radiant smiles, the South Australians found the ticket to their dream life when their beloved 1972 kombi 'Scout' unexpectedly landed in their lives in exchange for one simple thing - a promise to adventure.**

Meet Elise, a creative, free-spirited photo-journalist and her husband Dom, an ambitious entrepreneur, who run their organic winery *Down The Rabbit Hole* while living on the road and adventuring in their van around Australia.

Rewind a couple of years, and their lives were less than a gypset dream and more of an inner-city grind. They were time poor and working harder than ever to get their business off the ground, which only fuelled Elise's daydreams of travelling. In an unexpected twist of fate, their lives changed forever when they found their dream car, *Scout*.

They made a promise to escape their busy lives at least once a week - even to just recharge for few hours at the beach on a Sunday night. Soon these Sunday nights became their "moment of pause". The one moment in their week when time truly slowed down and they were able to disconnect from everything else, and connect with themselves and each other.

Stepping away from social expectations provided a whole new sense of clarity, perspective and incredible sense of freedom that they just wanted more of. Slowly those weekend getaways turned into weeks and then months, until the pair packed up and moved into *Scout* full-time.

**You are the most endearing couple, how did you two meet?** I was working at a bar in a hotel, saving up to move overseas. Four weeks before my flight out, Dom was brought in to manage the hotel's bar and restaurant. One day he walked up behind me when I was making a coffee, took hold of my hands from behind, and told me I wasn't making the coffee right. Despite him not being my 'type' and having very different outlooks on the world, there was an instant, very unexpected spark. I told him I was going travelling and wouldn't know how long I'd be gone for, and he told me he would be at the airport waiting for me when I got back. And a year later, he was. That was ten years ago and we've been married five years now.

**Ten years ago, what were your dreams?** I dreamed that in my late twenties I'd be single, travelling, and writing for a magazine, Lonely Planet or for TV, in a position that allowed me to travel and work. Dom's dream was to own a hotel and drive a Maserati. He wore nice suits every day, was incredibly ambitious, and dreamed of working for himself. Ten years ago, he probably would have used the word 'empire' when talking about his dreams and what he hoped to build.

**How did your dreams change after you met?** Looking at where we are now, it's like our aspirations and dreams have melted together, and reshaped both of us. Although we both had very different goals and ideas about our separate career paths, we made decisions the whole way along that were love-centred. We both made small sacrifices for each other, so that the other could follow their dreams. And those little sacrifices have actually ended up serving us, individually, and in turn as a team, more than we ever could have imagined and things just started to flow.

**Travel and wine, what a match. How did you come to own *Down The Rabbit Hole*?** Dom grew up making wine with his grandparents, who had previously owned vineyards in Italy. So he learned to make wine in the purest way. After owning a wine bar, and then a wine wholesale business, his break into his own winemaking game came through a wonderful friend and mentor, who suggested they started making Shiraz together. Fast-track five years and we are about to release our fifth wine.

**How did you go from running a winery to living on the road?** When we started *Down The Rabbit Hole*, every cent we had went into it and Dom was working harder than ever. We had just gotten married and I was in full support of him following his dream, but we barely had time together. I also began to worry that I would never get to do any of the travel I'd dreamed of doing in my twenties. I didn't want to leave him to go backpacking alone, so after much discussion, we came to a compromise. We'd buy a van so we could do short, affordable trips on weekends. And that's how the adventure began.

**So the adventure started when you got your van? We hear this is a pretty amazing story.** When I saw the ad online for *Scout*, I couldn't stop looking at it. A Westfalia camper in amazing condition, original interior, one owner since the day it was purchased in 1972. It was way out of our budget but somehow, I convinced Dom that we should "just look" at it. The van's owner Peter had purchased it together with his wife in in Germany just after they got married, and travelled all over Europe, South Africa, Australia and raised their family in it. We couldn't afford to put an offer in and left, but a week later he called and asked us to come back. He told us>

he'd had two offers, but both were collectors and he didn't want the van collecting dust in someone's shed. He loved the idea of it going to a young, newly married couple just beginning their lives together, just like him and his wife. So, he offered it to us at under half of what he was asking, on one condition. "You have to promise me you'll have adventures." There were many tears and we promised we would.

**And... you kept your promise?** Most days Dom was working 12 -14 hour days, and we had a lot going on. If we somehow had a weekend night free, the most attractive idea was to flop on the couch in front of the TV. However, we'd made a promise. Some weeks, it would mean us jumping in the van at 3pm on Sunday, driving an hour down the coast, pulling up somewhere, and then driving back at 6am Monday morning to start the work week.

These Sunday nights became this one moment in our weeks where time slowed down. Our one moment of pause. Instead of sitting on the couch in front of the telly, we would pull out our deck chairs and a bottle of wine, watch the sun go down, and then sit under the stars, either in silence or we'd talk and talk. We started having conversations we'd never had before. Instead of those few hours disappearing into the monotony of the week, they became these profound, memorable, and enriching moments. A time that we disconnected from everything else, and connected with each other, and with ourselves.

**How did you come to live on the road full-time?** Those Sunday nights became week-long trips, and then two-week-long trips, and finally a trip we called our 'Last Hoorah', a two month trip in the van, which was meant to be a break before we opened our cellar door, knuckled down, and worked hard. As Dom began regularly slowing down and pressing pause, for the first time in his life, he began to go within and discover a few things about himself that he'd never given himself a chance to. One day he turned to me and suggested we move into the van full-time, and give ourselves the time to really soak in what we were learning about ourselves and life.

**How has living on the road changed your life?** There is something about being on the road that allows us to tap into a slower gear in how we live and think. For us, it provides clarity, perspective, and an incredible sense of freedom. On many occasions I've found myself laying on a rug outside the van late at night, staring up at the most awesome starry skies. The first time I experienced it I remember thinking, "these stars are always here, we just can't see them". I feel that life on the road has allowed something similar to happen in our lives, to tap into something that's always there. We just fill our lives with so much busyness we might just miss it.

**You take such beautiful photos, how did photography become a passion?** I have an aunty who had travelled the world and as a kid I'd sit and flip through her photo albums and imagine the stories that went with them. I love what a photo can hold, it's like a ticket back in time to a moment paused forever that you get to keep. I want to capture every beautiful moment, and would take a photo of every single sunset if I could. So Dom made a rule, I am only allowed to have one day taking photos in each place. Every other sunset I have to just sit and enjoy with my eyes, unplug and soak it in a different way. Sometimes I find this rule hard, but I love him for it.

**What does pausing and slowing down mean to you?** Life is time. The more time we spend doing things that fill us with joy, that allow us to experience and know love in its fullness, the more fulfilling our lives will be. Pausing is about giving yourself a moment to check in, to go within, to work out what that is for you, or even to let an experience fully soak in. Pausing is about believing that you matter enough to give yourself the gift of time.

**Do you ever get stressed?** We still feel life's pressures, but I feel fairly confident saying we don't get overwhelmed anymore. This comes from what we've learned this past year and one thing we use to reset is the breath. If you ever feel yourself getting flustered, stressed, or anxious, take four deep, slow breaths. You hear people talk about using your breath as a tool a lot,

*Go somewhere you can see the stars*

and it's because it works. It slows your heart rate and your mind down, and gives you a brief moment to pause and recheck.

**What is your advice to others who need to recharge?** Next time you need a getaway, go somewhere where you can see the stars. When you get there, unplug. Turn off any device, turn off the WiFi. Disconnect, and give yourself the time to just be. We can't give you the formula, but we can promise that whatever flows for you from that state of being from giving yourself the time to go within, will be wonderous for you. It won't happen in an instant, but giving yourself the gift of time, a moment to dream your dreams, will be the greatest step towards living a fulfilling life.♥

To continue following this dreamy duo visit @elisecook and @domenicpalumbo

# week 30

*Date* ____ / ____ / ____

*Location* ____

My workload this week

Mischief I got up to

I really enjoyed

I didn't like

I'm glad that

Something I've recently mastered

# My favourite...

Person

Colour

Treat

Item in my wardrobe

Artist

Poet

Song to dance to

Happy place

Beach

Fruit

Flower

Drink

Part of my body

Catchphrase

Nickname

Scent

Magazine

Takeaway food

Possession

Exercise

Book

Cafe

Instagram account

Time of day

*there is only one life, and therefore it's perfect.*

-Paul Èluard

IMAGE: @LETMESEA

# week 31

*Date* / /

*Location*

Monday was

Tuesday I did

Wednesday I saw

Thursday I felt

Friday I went

Saturday I enjoyed

Sunday I relaxed by

Small wins I had this week

I was super productive when

Challenges I faced this week

The funniest thing that happened

New tunes I discovered

A project I'd like to start or finish next week

## critique me

*Receiving feedback isn't always easy, it's human nature to be offended and react defensively. But if you can learn to appreciate, embrace and invite feedback in all its forms: negative, positive or constructive, you'll become stronger, more self-aware and develop a healthy and balanced perspective of yourself. The more you practice asking people to give input into the areas of your life that you want to see develop, the more resilient you'll become.*

My best qualities

My not-so-great traits

Constructive feedback I've recently received

How open am I to taking on criticism?

Now... time to be critiqued! Ask a few people who are close to you to be completely honest.

1. What do you love or appreciate most about me?

2. What traits do you think I can work on to become a better person?

What people appreciate most about my personality

What others think I could improve on

What I learned from receiving this feedback

I'm going to work on

Sundays should come
with a pause button.

IMAGE: @ELISECOOK

# week 32

*Date* / /

*Location*

The most spontaneous thing I did this week

Best moments spent outside

Fun parties, events or gigs I attended

Friends I saw

New people I met

Time spent with family

I wish I was closer to

Birthdays I have coming up

Something thoughtful I can do for a friend's birthday

For my next birthday, I want to

*Flick to your bucket list and plan to tick something off!*

# Monthly Reflection

Something, someone or somewhere new

Moments that meant that little something extra

Am I kicking my soul goals? This month I've worked on

Something I regret

Something I've learned

Advice to myself for the next month

X X X

# week 33

*Date* ___ / ___ / ___

*Location* ___

My week was ___

I was curious about ___

I got distracted by ___

I was super tired when ___

I was impressed by ___

I got upset when ___

I was pumped to ___

The most impressive meal I ate this week

Something new I discovered

I'm a ☐ night owl ☐ early bird

I usually go to bed at ______ and wake up at ______. On average, I sleep ______ hours each night.

My most productive time of the day is

I procrastinate over

My focuses for next week are

# pause.

*Thoughts. Words. Scribbles. Pictures.*

# week
# 34

*Date* / /

*Location*

This week was

I discovered

I found it tough to

My exercise this week was

My favourite training buddy is

A moment I wish I could relive

# My current state of mind

**I'd like to tell my...**

Mum

Dad

Grandma/grandpa

Sibling

Best friend

Lover / Crush

*Go on and tell them how you feel!*

There's always something deeply satisfying about watching a sunrise or sunset. Make a point of catching one this week.

week

# 35

*Date* ___/___/___

*Location* ______

Seven moments I remember from the last week

Someone I thought a lot about this week

The most satisfying thing I worked on

I felt content when

I felt unfairly treated by

I lost track of time when

Something I want to start doing

## my environmental footprint

*We're fortunate to live on this big, beautiful planet, but so many of our simple daily tasks (like driving to work or doing a load of laundry) leave a destructive footprint. So how can we save it from ourselves? The first step is to pause and take an honest look at our own environmental footprints. Do you use a keep-cup for your coffee? How much water are you wasting every day? It may not seem like much, but if we all do our bit for the environment, we can make a huge difference. It all starts and ends with us.*

How aware am I of my impact on the environment? ______________________________

______________________________

______________________________

______________________________

| **Do I...** | Yes | Sometimes | No |
|---|---|---|---|
| Recycle | ☐ | ☐ | ☐ |
| Use a KeepCup for takeaway drinks | ☐ | ☐ | ☐ |
| Use the sunshine instead of the dryer | ☐ | ☐ | ☐ |
| Only use cold water in the washing machine | ☐ | ☐ | ☐ |
| Take reusable bags to the grocery store | ☐ | ☐ | ☐ |
| Say no to straws / use a reusable straw | ☐ | ☐ | ☐ |
| Say no to plastics like bottles, containers and bags | ☐ | ☐ | ☐ |
| Use biodegradable / reusable trash bags | ☐ | ☐ | ☐ |
| Walk, cycle or use public transport to work | ☐ | ☐ | ☐ |
| Eat seasonal, local and organic food as often as possible | ☐ | ☐ | ☐ |
| Receive paperless bills | ☐ | ☐ | ☐ |
| Keep showers to under 10 minutes | ☐ | ☐ | ☐ |
| Turn the tap off when I brush my teeth | ☐ | ☐ | ☐ |
| Turn lights and appliances off when not using them | ☐ | ☐ | ☐ |
| Use natural cleaning products | ☐ | ☐ | ☐ |

Other ways I'm helping the environment

Considering the above, what are some things I could start doing?

New habits I am committed to adopt for a more sustainable life

# week 36

*Date* / /

*Location*

The highlights of this week

The lowlights

I'm grateful for

I'm super excited about

The last time I lied was

because

The last time I caught someone lying

it made me feel

When do I lie? Why? What would it be like to never lie and only ever tell the truth?

**stop, rewind & record**

# *Monthly Reflection*

Something, someone or somewhere new

Moments that meant that little something extra

Am I kicking my soul goals? This month I've worked on

I was inspired by

Something I've learned

Advice to myself for the next month

**X X X**

*Date* ___ / ___ / ___

*Location* ___

# week 37

Five magic moments this week

1 ___

2 ___

3 ___

4 ___

5 ___

Something I wanted to do this week, but skipped ___

Why I skipped it and how it affected my week ___

# *If... (and why)*

I could speak any language, I'd choose

I could master any skill, I would

I had to eat one food for a whole week, I'd choose

My house was on fire and I could only save one thing, it would be

I was an animal, I'd like a

I could change one thing in the world, I would

I could be another person for a week, I'd like to be

I could live in another era, I'd live in

I had to move countries, I'd want to live in

Someone knows me well, they know I'd never

I could meet anyone in the world, I'd like to meet

I could have the answer to one question, I'd love to know

to hell with happy endings
you are here for the story
-Beau Taplin

IMAGE: @LIZROSA

# week 38

*Date* ____ / ____ / ____

*Location* ________

## This week I...

Learned

Saw

Visited

Admired

Adventured

Watched

Wrote

Tasted

Was surprised by

Exercised

Kissed

Decided

Contacted

Walked

Cooked

Tried

# My Rituals...

In the mornings, I

My nights are spent

On the weekends, I mostly

To keep myself balanced, I

New things I want to implement into my routine

Quote of the week

If you're lucky to have your grandparents or parents in your life, set a time to chat with them this week and ask them about what their life was like when they were your age.

# week 39

*Date* / /

*Location*

The best day this week was

A day that didn't go so well

Somewhere/something new I explored

Exercise I did

My diet was

A great book I read or podcast I listened to

My work/life balance currently is

Things I would like to implement to feel more balanced

How present am I with the people I am around? *(Do I really pay them attention or am I distracted by phone, work, other thoughts?)*

How good are my listening skills? *(Do I actually listen and try to understand what someone is telling me or do I pre-empt my answers?)*

Moments I valued the most this week

**The one thing that you have that nobody else has is you. Your voice, your mind, your story, your vision. So write and draw and build and play and dance and live as only you can.** - *Neil Gaiman*

# between the lines

*"Soon enough, we will all be bones in the ground, the oceans will dry up, the sun will burn out and nobody will be around to remember we were here at all. So go, spend your time here with heart. Find what matters to you and manifest it while you can. Because while this universe we inhabit may be infinite and unfeeling, we are not, and that is our gift."*

**These are the stirringly beautiful words of Beau Taplin, Australian author and instagram sensation, whose raw, heartfelt and relatable poetry gently invites us to pause and contemplate the world around us.**

Raised in a small Australian country town, Beau grew up as a curious, nature-loving kid. He was drawn to fantasy books full of enchanted forests and treasure hoarding-dragons, awakening his fascination for language at a young age. As he grew older, a deep obsession for the unknown kept him in search of ways to express the magical moments he witnessed in his own reality. It was in 2014 when, intrigued by the impact his words could have on others, he began sharing his philosophical thoughts on life, love and the human spirit online.

Now published across seven books, his words have been quoted by celebrities, tattooed on bodies and shared by hundreds of thousands of people. The vulnerability of Beau's poetry cuts through the chaos of a visual platform like Instagram, reminding us all that there is courage in pressing pause and exploring the world within.

**Beau, your work is so heartfelt and raw, you have such a beautiful way of shaping your emotions into words. Where do you draw inspiration from?**
I think it is mostly drawn from experience, I tend to move through life in extremes and I have always searched for the stories in moments. The thing that partly inspires me to write is that it is my clearest mode of expression, the best way I have of showing the outside world my truest self. I think that's probably a deep part of why we all do the things we love, but also I think because I am so charmed by the impact a few chosen words can really have on a person, their power to bring comfort or even change to the course of a life. So much of who I am has been shaped by great writing. If I could ever make an impact like that on others, to me that's a thing worth pursuing.

**Did you always know you wanted to be a writer?**
Well, as a child I wanted to be like Sam Neill from Jurassic Park and dig up dusty old dinosaur bones. But I have always been interested in language, particularly language that could capture the magic or metaphysical and make it real. I spent a lot of time quietly reading as a kid and I was always drawn to fantasy. In my adulthood I began to appreciate the fact that all of these archetypal forces are symbolic of real truths in our own lives, and so this deep obsession for the unknown progressed to one of learning to properly witness the magic in everyday life and and then attempting to capture these powerful moments in words.

**So your childhood had quite a big impact on your work?** I was raised in Lilydale, a small town in the far east of Melbourne, where the suburbs meet the farmlands. I recall many moments spent wandering through nature or travelling out to the country as a child to visit my cousins. My parents marriage splintered when I was twelve, and I am still working to figure out the consequences or impact that may or may not have had, but while I remember tough times and many deep challenges, I think back on those years as the sculpting tool that shaped the core of who I am.

**You now have a huge social media following, how did this all start?** The first platform I ever posted writing to was Myspace. I am that ancient. Haha. But Tumblr was where I started to write for reasons other than only personal. One afternoon I decided to post something to my instagram account, at the time I remember feeling unsure if it was the right kind of content for this kind of platform, but people responded powerfully and I still can't believe how fortunate I am to have the readers I do.

**Your work has clearly become a great success. What does being 'successful' mean to you?**
Success to me is feeling worthwhile in the world, whatever form that might take. It's a silent agreement between you and your inner self that the thing you have chosen to pursue each day matters. I think success is so often associated with fame or material wealth, but anyone who has acquired these things knows all too well that they are utterly meaningless, and even dismantling, without diligent inner work.

**What do you want to achieve with your work?**
There are many admirable people out there who are driven by virtuous, large-scale pursuits, saving the world's oceans, easing the earth of suffering or war, bringing about dramatic change, and thank the stars for them. But for me, it has always been the small things that drive me, the close bonds between friends, tales of romance and adventure, feeling totally, >

*Your body is not a temple. Temples can be destroyed and desecrated.*
*Your body is a forest – thick canopies of maple trees and sweet-scented wildflowers sprouting in the undergrowth.*
*You will grow back, over and over, no matter how badly you are devastated.*

utterly present in a moment and all the untold joy that brings. I'm very much about encouraging and describing the passions of life at the individual level, learning to see the stories in all things, and aligning yourself perfectly in tune with the universe.

**Where's your favourite place to write?** Either the warmth and quiet of my room in the morning, or the thick, stirring atmosphere of a bar at night, someplace uncrowded with a fireplace in the corner.

**So what bar will we find you at?** My local (Melbourne) favourites would be *Neptune* for writing or romance and certainly *Two Wrongs* for wicked, unapologetic fun.

**What does 'pause' mean to you?** Interestingly for a word that can so often refer to stagnancy, pause for me brings to mind images of fluent movement. When we are still, we travel the roads of our inner selves, we explore our unconscious and map out the terrain, giving us a clearer picture of who it is we truly are. It is to meet with your deepest, truest self and ask it all the tough questions. To take pause is often the boldest, bravest action we can take, and I think that's an important one to remember.

**Do you feel that poetry makes people pause?** In a deeply meaningful way, I believe they are one in the same. The act of reading poetry is an exercise of self-reflection and discovery. When you read you are in a one-on-one conversation with yourself, you are setting aside time to pause and reflect, and I think that's an important component in nurturing a more centred self.

**What's your favourite poem?** *O me. O Life.* by the poet Walt Whitman. The poem's final line, "The powerful play goes on, and you may contribute a verse" really is a core tenet to my own manifesto and what I believe a life is all about, to make a meaningful mark on the world with the time we are given, and leave the earth a touch or two more beautiful than we found it.

**Pen and paper or digital?** Pen and paper for free, spontaneous thought and digital for deep, creative work. I perfect and edit a great deal of my writings and digital is a simpler space for that.

**Tell us about one of your best adventures.** I booked a spontaneous trip to Europe one late Tuesday evening and I was on a plane a week later. Everything that could go wrong did. And I wouldn't have it any other way. I went from hotels with butlers to backpacker floors. I knelt by Tolkien's gravestone in Oxford and shot the cover for Bloom.

I watched an artist sing in the window sill of a tall, narrow loft in Amsterdam, then ended up on the entirely wrong train back to London, missing the terrible incident in Brussels by only a few hours. I made a good friend who owned a vacant house back home in Melbourne, which then became my home shortly after I returned. But this doesn't even scratch the surface. Those two short weeks were non-stop chaos and changed my life for the better - teaching me how to feel present and be courageous in life again.

**What's your favourite possession?** A painting my mother did of me back in 2010. I can see her nurturing love in every brushstroke and it always brings me warmth when I need it most.

**A book you'd recommend to everyone?** *The Upanishads*, ancient Sanskrit texts that are a collection of philosophical thoughts and principles that are still more than relevant today. It has been a work that has really awakened me to the fact that humanity has always carried all the answers to a well-lived life deep down within us, and it is up to the artists and philosophers of the world to translate these core truths into the language of our times and remind us of them when we lose our way.

**Tell us something we don't know about you.**
I like to cook. I'm not any good, but ever since writing became my daily work I needed another way to be, let's say, carelessly creative. Basically, I love making a mess in the kitchen.

Also, I was a songwriter before I was a writer. I wrote lyrics and melodies for a few different artists, but mostly for a band with my younger brother. Man, it broke my heart when that all came to an end, but all the lessons I learned through music over the years really paved the way for everything I've managed since.

**Any advice to budding authors?** A close friend once spoke to me about the importance of cultivating a careful balance between the artist and the craftsman in you. The artist is your passion, your creativity unrestrained and ungoverned by any demand outside of your own heart. The craftsman is your structure, the responsibility to meet the expectations set by yourself and by others. The craftsman finds a space for your art in the world and fills it. When you're too much craftsman, the art becomes soulless. Conversely, when you give the artist too much control, it's just not sustainable, inevitably you grow resentful, full of self-doubt, or worse.

**Words of wisdom you would like to share.**
You know what to do. The big secret is every one of us comes complete with an extensive instruction manual to life and that manual is called the intuition, listen closely to it. We really do need to give ourselves more credit. We are far more wise and powerful than we believe we are.♥

**Write** - *the truth.*
**Remember** - *the miracle of existence.*
**Identify** - *your faulty software.*
**Take** - *your deepest pains into your warm embrace, then set them free.*
**Erase** - *the belief that it is ever too late.*

Find more of Beau's beautiful words and book collection @beautaplin

# week 40

*Date* / /

*Location*

Emotions of the week

The highlights

Unexpected moments

Intimate moments

I've felt connected too

Kind things I've done this week

# Astrology & Spirituality...

My sun (star) sign is

*Characteristics*

My moon sign is

*Characteristics*

My rising sign is

*Characteristics*

Spirituality: What do I believe in?

When we die, I think we

stop, rewind & record

# Monthly Reflection

Something, someone or somewhere new

Moments that meant that little something extra

Am I kicking my soul goals? This month I've worked on

Someone I can reach out to for guidance to achieve my goals?

Something I've learned

Advice to myself for the next month

X X X

# week 41

*Date* ____ / ____ / ____

*Location* ____

Things I've loved doing this week

Things I've loved cooking or creating

Time I loved spending with my loved ones

Time I loved spending alone

Things that currently make me happy and excited about life

Things that are tough and bringing me down

Things I wish I could change

Simple moments I treasure

# courage

*So many of us are held back from achieving our dreams and reaching our full potential by fear. A fear of speaking up, fear of change, fear of judgement, fear of failure. When fear creeps in, it can shatter confidence and leave talents, hopes and wishes unfulfilled. But, if you dare to face your fears and pursue your deepest desires, you'll open a whole new world of possibilities.*

Picture yourself being 80 years old, what would you regret not having done?

If I wasn't afraid I would...

**RELATIONSHIPS**

**CAREER**

**LIFESTYLE**

**ADVENTURE**

What's stopping me from doing some of these things right now?

A few steps I can take to overcome my fears

One thing I've always been afraid of, that I'm now excited to pursue

**You change the world by being yourself.** - *Yoko Ono*

I feel alive out here.
@CHRISTIANSCHAFFER

# week 42

*Date* / /

*Location*

The beginning of the week was

On the weekend I

Something that surprised me

Something that excited me

Something that annoyed me

Something I always want to remember

## Qualities I admire in the people I'm surrounded by...

Name

What I admire in him/her

Name

What I admire in him/her

Name

What I admire in him/her

How I think people perceive me

The things I want to embrace

*Thoughts. Words. Scribbles. Pictures.*

love.

Date ___ / ___ / ___

Location ___

# week 43

This week was ☐ relaxed ☐ a bit stressed ☐ full on ☐ just perfect

I spent most of my days ___

I felt proud of myself when ___

I absolutely loved ___

I treated myself with ___

I felt beautiful when ___

I currently work

What I love about it

What I'd like to change

People who have reached the goals I strive for

What can I learn from them?

What am I naturally gifted at?

What am I not so good at? *(and can admit)*

Something I'd like to improve

A compliment I often receive

*Date* ____/____/____

*Location* ____

# week 44

## This week, I...

Felt great when ____

Spent quality time with ____

Loved working on ____

Enjoyed cooking ____

Had lots of fun with ____

Got sweaty ____

Took time to ____

Slept ____

Something I've been meaning *(but never get time)* to...

Fix

Get checked up

Tell someone

Organise

Explore

Read

Watch

Cook

Try

I procrastinate a lot over

How much time do I spend on social media a day?

Three overdue projects I am committed to getting done *(any of the above?)*

**stop, rewind & record**

# *Monthly Reflection*

Something, someone or somewhere new

Moments that meant that little something extra

Am I kicking my soul goals? This month I've worked on

Something I regret

Something I've learned

Killer advice to myself for the next month/going forward

X X X

week
# 45

*Date* / /

*Location*

## This week's favourite moments...

At home

At work

Outside

With a friend

On the road

On the phone

# My home is...

Something I'd like to change about it

In life, I'm most passionate about

My dream lifestyle is

A road trip I want to go on

A person I'd like to get to know better

Something I could have handled better recently

## my legacy

*Who are you? What do you stand for? What fulfils you? What are your values? When you leave this earth, what do you want to be remembered for?*

What are the core values that are most important for me to portray and uphold?

Do the people closest to me uphold these same values?

Ten things I love doing and without them, my life would feel unfulfilled

If my life were to end tomorrow, what would I regret not doing, seeing or accomplishing?

What do I want to be remembered for? *(Remember, it's not just about what you want to accomplish. People don't always remember what you did, but they always remember how you made them feel.)*

Little things I could start doing to make it happen

# My achievements...

*From big accomplishments (like graduating, moving interstate or being promoted) to the smaller moments that might not seem like much at the time (like overcoming a fear, helping a friend through a hard time, travelling solo or learning a language), it's so easy to lose sight of just how much cool sh*t we've done. Take some time to jot down all of the positive moments and achievements that have shaped your path and led you to where you are today.*

*Date* ___ / ___ / ___

*Location* ___

# week 46

## This week, did I...

Wake up in the morning feeling energised? *(If not, why?)*

Put enough effort into my relationships?

Take care of myself physically and mentally?

Use my time wisely?

Watch the sunset / sunrise?

Take time to relax?

Count my blessings?

Make someone smile? *(Who?)*

In the news this week

Celebrity/public figure I admire at the moment? *(Why?)*

TV shows I've loved lately

Plays, gigs or shows I've seen, or want to see

Something I've been open-minded about lately

Something I've been close-minded about

Someone I've been unfair to

Someone I've felt unfairly treated by

Something I'd like to tell my 18-year-old self

Nobody is you
and that is your
superpower.

Date ____ / ____ / ____

Location ____

# week 47

## Something / Someone...

Strange I saw

Funny I heard

I visited

That made me stressed

That bothered me

I missed

I cuddled

I adored

Something I think about a lot

The last time I pushed the boundaries of my comfort zone

What excites me most about the future?

What worries me most about the future?

*Declutter challenge:* Every day this week, recycle, donate or give something away that you don't need in your home. At the end of the month, you'll have gotten rid of 28 items and your life will feel less cluttered.

WORDS + IMAGE: @WILLANDBEAR

keep it slow.

# week 48

*Date* ____ / ____ / ____

*Location*

A positive thing that happened this week

A negative thing that happened

A cool thing that happened

An event I enjoyed

Something I did out of habit

Something I did out of care

Someone that made me feel loved

A moment I want to relive

A moment I lingered a little longer

The best thing I bought

A song I sang

An obstacle I faced

The best news I received

Bars / restaurants / cafes I visited

Performance I saw / want to see

The nicest thing I did for someone

The nicest thing someone did for me

My health is

If I could go back a month in time, what advice would I give myself?

**stop, rewind & record**

# Monthly Reflection

Something, someone or somewhere new

Moments that meant that little something extra

Am I kicking my soul goals? This month I've worked on

I was inspired by

Something I've learned

Advice to myself for the next month

X X X

# week 49

*Date* / /

*Location*

Routine things I've done this week

Things I've done outside of my normal routine

An interesting conversation I had

Someone that made me smile

A loving gesture I received

What I love about my room

What I'd like to change

When do I worry about what others think?

What have I been avoiding out of fear?

How is life asking me to grow right now?

How open am I to people's thoughts, opinions and different ways of living?

What brings me joy?

**Your time is limited, so don't waste it living someone else's life.** - *Steve Jobs*

# Trash tribe

*making sustainable waves down under*

**Meet Nat and Dan, all-round legends who are saving our oceans, one piece of plastic at a time. When the two first met, they had no idea their romantic weekend getaways and mutual love of the ocean would inspire a huge, nationwide movement.**

As a newly loved-up couple, Nat and Dan often took time to pause from their hectic 9-5 grind with coastal getaways, always in search of the next secluded beach to wash away the work week and reconnect with nature. Thinking they'd be surfing at postcard-worthy beaches away from the crowds, they instead found something far less picturesque. Weekend-after-weekend, they were heartbroken to find an alarming amount of trash and plastic washed ashore along their beloved Australian coastline.

Being passionate ocean lovers, the couple were also shocked that no one in their surfing community was talking about the problem. They couldn't ignore that they were literally swimming in plastic, so they started to run small events where they rallied friends together and spent the day clearing trash at the beach.

But it wasn't until they embarked on a seven month road trip around Australia that the devastation of our man-made waste really hit home. As they dived deeper into the problem, they knew they had to do something about it. And so, the *Clean Coast Collective* was born.

Inspired by their weekly pauses in nature, their simple beach clean-ups have now evolved into a nationwide trash tribe initiative, committed to cleaning up beaches around the country and raising awareness to stop plastic use at the source. To date, the movement has collectively cleared a whopping ten tonnes of trash from Australian shorelines, and this eco-conscious couple are certainly making sustainable waves Down Under.

**Nat and Dan, thank you so much for your massive efforts in cleaning up our planet. Tell us more about the *Clean Coast Collective* and what you guys are all about.** *Clean Coast Collective* is a non-profit organisation, committed to stopping plastics at the source, and cleaning up the plastic we've already littered. To truly solve this issue, we all need to stop relying on disposable plastics, so we've designed lifestyle accessories that replace the cheap and toxic single-use plastics in your life with timeless alternatives.

There are still five trillion tonnes of plastics floating at sea, that's why 100% of profits from our products go directly towards funding our signature 'Trash Tribe' expeditions. Each year, we take groups of creative and inspiring Australians to clean up some of Australia's most polluted beaches - these beaches are all remote, making the journey a once-in-a-lifetime experience.

**Where did your passion for the environment come from?** I've always been passionate about it. I grew up with a family who spent a lot of time at the beach, bushwalking and rock climbing in the National Parks around our hometown. At university, I always studied something that had to do with the environment and did internships with non-for profit organisations. When I met Dan we were both working in the government in very unsexy, professional jobs, and I think we were both looking for something to do that was more meaningful than our corporate nine-to-fives.

**Tell us how your beach clean-ups got started.** When we started dating, we loved getting away from the city and spent our weekends down the South Coast of New South Wales. We were shocked seeing the amount of plastic washing up on the shores, so we started looking deeper into the issue and learned that it takes hundreds of years to break down. The fact that it's littered all over beaches around the world and that no one we surfed with even talked about it, just blew us away. We started to learn about the damage it's doing to the environment and we just couldn't ignore it, so we started to take bags with us whenever we went surfing to clean it up. That's when we had the idea to organise a beach clean-up with our friends.

**What happened on the first beach clean up?** The very first clean up we did in 2014 was super low key. We thought it would just be nice to all hang out on the beach together and do something good, so we asked a bunch of friends to come down and help us clean some trash. I think like eight of us showed up. We thought it was really cool and nicknamed ourselves the *Trash Tribe*.

We started to take photos and record what we cleaned up on instagram, and from there we registered as a non-for-profit like responsible adults! We organised a few more clean-ups before we decided to travel further to see what it was like around the rest of the country. We headed off in a four-wheel drive for seven months where we met and talked to locals, conservation groups, rangers and surfers. That's when we first saw how big the issue was in remote parts of the country.

**We love the idea of your Trash Tribe. What's involved?** We run expeditions where we spend the week cleaning up a heavily polluted beach. We travel to extremely remote, wild and beautiful parts of the country that are hard to access but filled with rubbish washed ashore by cyclones, currents from South East Asia, or lost overboard from big ships.

We camp for the entire journey - it's hot, stinky, dusty and so much fun. Each member of the Trash Tribe must commit to running a project when they return from the trip to share their experience and knowledge with their community - this is our way of spreading awareness of coastal pollution in remote Australia to as many pockets of the population as possible. All the information from what we collect then goes into *The Australian Marine Debris Database* to help find solutions for how to stop plastic pollution in the future. >

Three ways to make a difference...

1. Always use a reusable coffee cup, bag and straw
2. Buy locally grown organic food.
3. Use bamboo toothbrushes.

**What's one of the best part of one of these trips?** The emotional journey that everyone goes on their first time. Usually the participants are so angry about how much rubbish there is, and then as we start to remove the trash, we see how inspired and committed they become towards making a change to the environment.

**What impact does plastic have and how is it damaging our planet today?** Plastics are full of toxins and aren't reusable. When they enter the ocean, they don't break down. We only use a straw or takeaway container for a few minutes, but they stay in the environment for hundreds of years. One study predicted that there will be more plastic in the sea than fish by 2050. And, there is more and more research coming out about how plastic impacts our health. Our landfills are filling up and nothing can break down, and China has recently stopped accepting Australia's recycling. It's a problem that isn't going away and will continue to get worse and worse. The key solution is to use less plastic in the first place and recycle what we do use.

**What are some simple things we all can do to help the environment?** It's all about making good choices whenever you can, one step at a time, wherever you can. Be mindful with what you do and everything you buy - think about what your money is supporting and where your money is coming from. You will ultimately make better decisions when you're aware of how you live on this planet. For example, buying organic fruit and veg is not only healthy for you, but it's healthier for the earth because it's not sprayed with pesticides and hasn't been trucked around the country. Before you buy something, weigh up whether you actually need it and try support sustainable fashion brands. They can only continue to grow if we support them.

***Clean Coast Collective* is a non-for-profit organisation - is there anything else you do for a living?** We are very blessed to live here (in Byron Bay), where we run our eco-conscious coworking space *The Corner Palm*. It's a beautiful, creative space filled with people running their own business and following their dreams. From here we run *Clean Coast Collective* on the side and have our own freelance jobs as well. Dan is in finance and I do marketing and branding for a sustainable building company. We just try to live a solid life up here, and make sure that we work to live rather than living to work.

**Running two businesses and freelance jobs - you must be busy! How do you take time out to pause?** We really try not to work on weekends and when we leave the studio, we relax and spend time with friends. We don't have internet at home so we have that downtime and always turn our phones off at night. We also try to get to the ocean daily, even if it's just ducking to the beach at sunset to get away from our desks, away from the 'to-do' list. I guess it's such a calming place for us. It's humbling, puts things into perspective that you're just one person on one big giant planet. It's something that is very grounding and slows us down. We can have the most stressful days but if we go for a walk or jump in the ocean, we just wash the day away.

**Why do you love spending time in nature?** We find that we spend so much time being fed information - listening to the radio and podcasts, that there isn't much time to stop and think "what do I really want to be spending my life doing?" We never pause to be in our own thoughts enough. In nature we don't use technology which truly slows us down.

**What has been your wildest experience during a clean up?** As we visit extremely remote beaches, the whole trips are pretty wild. Last time we had a crocodile who was watching us the whole time. We usually see one every year, but never on the beach.

**What is the weirdest thing you've found during a clean up?** Once we found a children's plastic playground slide - other groups have found prosthetic legs.

**If you could choose any other job in the world, what would it be?** I'd love to just get a job planting trees one day a week - get off the computer and outside!

**Is there a dream beach you'd like to go to?** There are some incredibly beaches in Hawaii we'd like to take a *Trash Tribe* to.

**When it comes to recycling, how important is it to sort your trash?** Really important - but we like to remind people that recycling is not the first step. Start by reducing as much waste as possible and then recycle after that. The problem begins with how much trash we are putting out on the curb.

**What is the ultimate goal for *Clean Coast Collective*?** The real dream is that we do not have to exist anymore! In the meantime, we're aiming to have constant impact so we can convince more and more people to change their habits. ♥

Check out @cleancoastcollective for more tips or to join the trash tribe yourself.

Date ___ / ___ / ___

Location ___

# week 50

This week's achievements

I was entertained by

What's my intuition been trying to tell me?

The last time a kid made me laugh was

The last time I played

A sport or activity I've always wanted to try

I haven't done it because

Things I miss from my childhood

The things that matter most in my life

A habit I need to let go of

We live in a universe full of galaxies, clouds, planets and stars. Next week, spend a night stargazing and make a wish upon a shooting star!

# week
# 51

Date ____/____/____

Location ____

This week has been ____

I smiled when ____

Little things that worried me ____

I loved watching ____

What I lacked or missed this week ____

When it comes to my head, heart and gut, I mostly listen to ____

Something I'm trying to understand ____

How present was I with the people I caught up with? ____

*Were you distracted by your phone?*

Someone that deserves a big thank you ____

## *This week I...*

Created

Regretted

Drooled over

Couldn't believe

Realised

Was in love with

## My...

Ultimate adventure

Favourite quote

Favourite wine

Favourite chocolate

Harshest critic

Hidden talent

What am I most grateful for in my life right now?

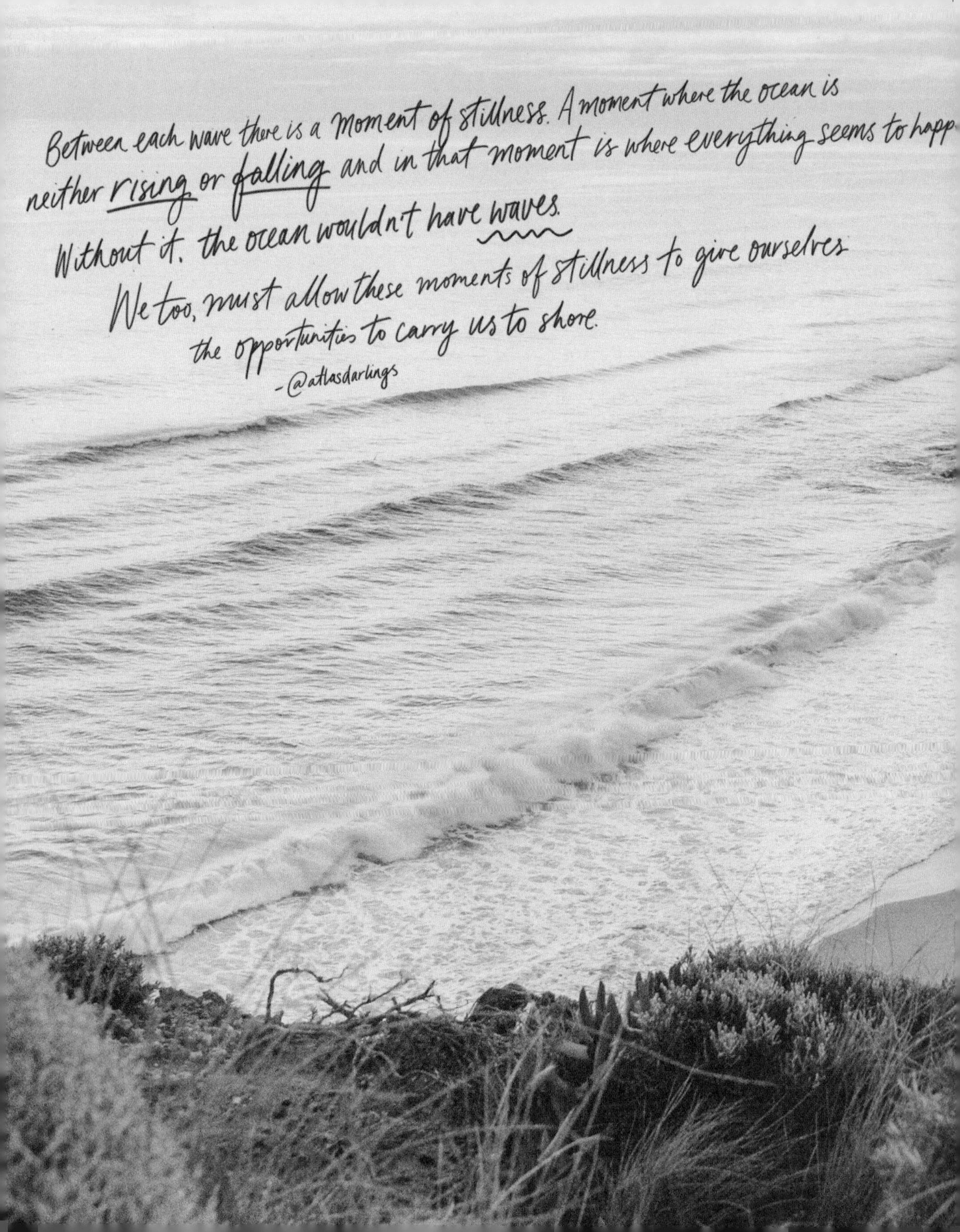
Between each wave there is a Moment of stillness. A moment where the ocean is
neither rising or falling and in that moment is where everything seems to happ
Without it, the ocean wouldn't have waves.
We too, must allow these moments of stillness to give ourselves
the opportunities to carry us to shore.
-@atlasdarlings

IMAGE: @ATLASDARLINGS

Date ___/___/___

Location ___

# week 52

Week 52 has been ___

Fun things I got up to ___

The most captivating story I heard ___

12 months have passed since I started taking time to pause weekly. I've ...

Noticed ___

Learned ___

Changed ___

In the next twelve months, I want to make sure I...

________________ more, and ________________ less

Visit ________________

________________

Enjoy ________________

________________

Cook ________________

________________

See more ________________

________________

Spend time ________________

________________

Take ________________

________________

Stop ________________

________________

Start ________________

________________

The mark I want to leave on this world ________________

________________

________________

________________

________________

________________

# My 52 weeks *in summary...*

The best adventures I had in the last 52 weeks

The people I got to know

The biggest achievement of this year

Hardships I faced / Most challenging times

Something I did this year that I'd never done before

Something I wish I'd done more of

Something I wish I'd done less of

Something I really wanted, and got

Something I wanted, but didn't get

Mistakes I made

Life changing moments

I felt the most alive when

How well did I take care of my body, mind, and soul?

Projects that I completed

The most inspiring person I met

The nicest thing someone did for me

Did I fall in or out of love?

Bars/ restaurants I frequented

Song that will always remind me of this year

## The best...

Book I read

Movie / TV Show I watched

Live performance I saw

New thing I tried

Compliment I received

Place I woke up

Night/s out

Place I discovered

Date night

Advice I've received

My birthday was spent

Soul goals I ticked off

The most valuable lessons I learned

Something/s that I need to let go of

If I could travel back to the beginning of the year, the advice I would give myself

## Goals, ambitions and dreams for next year...

# my bucketlist

*101 things I want to do with my one wild & precious life*

1 ☐
2 ☐
3 ☐
4 ☐
5 ☐
6 ☐
7 ☐
8 ☐
9 ☐
10 ☐
11 ☐
12 ☐
13 ☐
14 ☐
15 ☐
16 ☐
17 ☐
18 ☐
19 ☐
20 ☐
21 ☐
22 ☐
23 ☐
24 ☐

24 ☐
26 ☐
27 ☐
28 ☐
29 ☐
30 ☐
31 ☐
32 ☐
33 ☐
34 ☐
35 ☐
36 ☐
37 ☐
38 ☐
39 ☐
40 ☐
41 ☐
42 ☐
43 ☐
44 ☐
45 ☐
46 ☐
47 ☐
48 ☐

49 ☐

50 ☐

51 ☐

52 ☐

53 ☐

54 ☐

55 ☐

56 ☐

57 ☐

58 ☐

59 ☐

60 ☐

61 ☐

62 ☐

63 ☐

64 ☐

65 ☐

66 ☐

67 ☐

68 ☐

69 ☐

70 ☐

71 ☐

72 ☐

73 ☐

74 ☐

75 ☐

76 ☐

77 ☐

78 ☐

79 ☐

80 ☐

81 ☐

82 ☐

83 ☐

84 ☐

85 ☐

86 ☐

87 ☐

88 ☐

89 ☐

90 ☐

91 ☐

92 ☐

93 ☐

94 ☐

95 ☐

96 ☐

97 ☐

98 ☐

99 ☐

100 ☐

101 ☐

*"To live as if we are dying gives us a chance to experience some real presence." - Anne Lammot*

*To be continued...*